Pirate Paul & Ana Mae Mouse Show Me

The Twelve Months of™

The United States of

America

Original songs available online at...
www.thepeartreepress.com

Words and Illustrations by AnnieMarie E. Chiaverilla
Edited by Kirk Nelson

The Peartree Press™

Handwritten inscription: For Emmett & Miles — Adventure awaits the curious... keep reading! 7/22/23

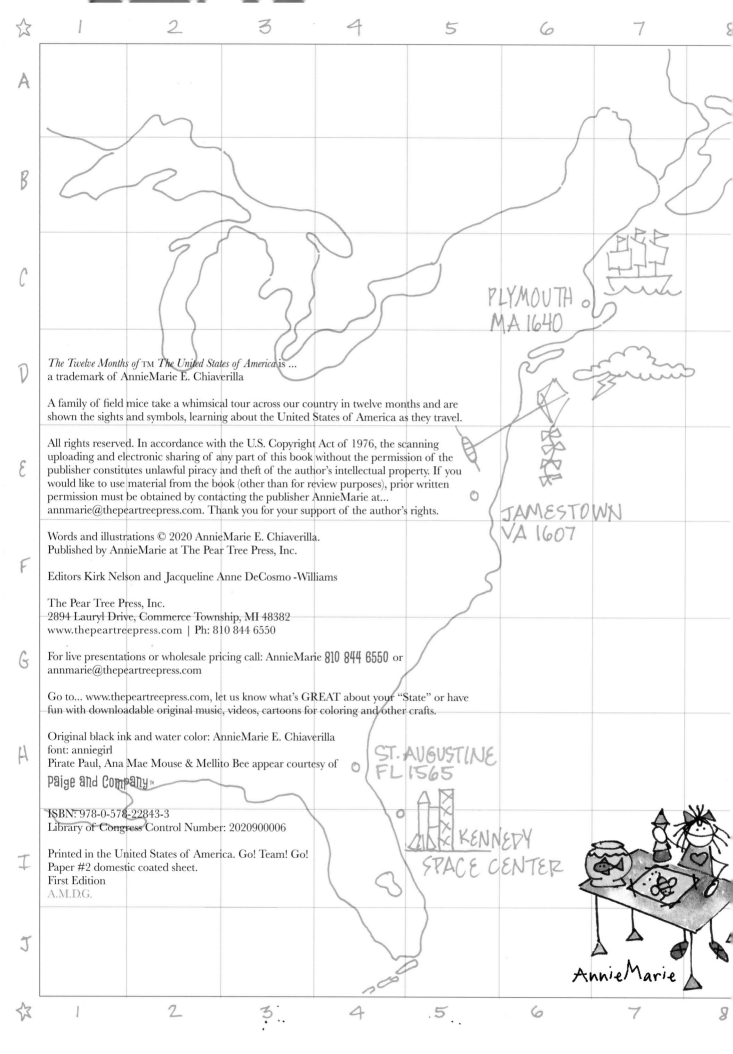

The Twelve Months of ™ *The United States of America* is ...
a trademark of AnnieMarie E. Chiaverilla

A family of field mice take a whimsical tour across our country in twelve months and are shown the sights and symbols, learning about the United States of America as they travel.

Words and illustrations © 2020 AnnieMarie E. Chiaverilla.
Published by AnnieMarie at The Pear Tree Press, Inc.

Editors Kirk Nelson and Jacqueline Anne DeCosmo -Williams

The Pear Tree Press, Inc.
2894 Lauryl Drive, Commerce Township, MI 48382
www.thepeartreepress.com | Ph: 810 844 6550

For live presentations or wholesale pricing call: AnnieMarie 810 844 6550 or annmarie@thepeartreepress.com

Go to... www.thepeartreepress.com, let us know what's GREAT about your "State" or have fun with downloadable original music, videos, cartoons for coloring and other crafts.

Original black ink and water color: AnnieMarie E. Chiaverilla
font: anniegirl
Pirate Paul, Ana Mae Mouse & Mellito Bee appear courtesy of
Paige and Company ™

ISBN: 978-0-578-22843-3
Library of Congress Control Number: 2020900006

Printed in the United States of America. Go! Team! Go!
Paper #2 domestic coated sheet.
First Edition
A.M.D.G.

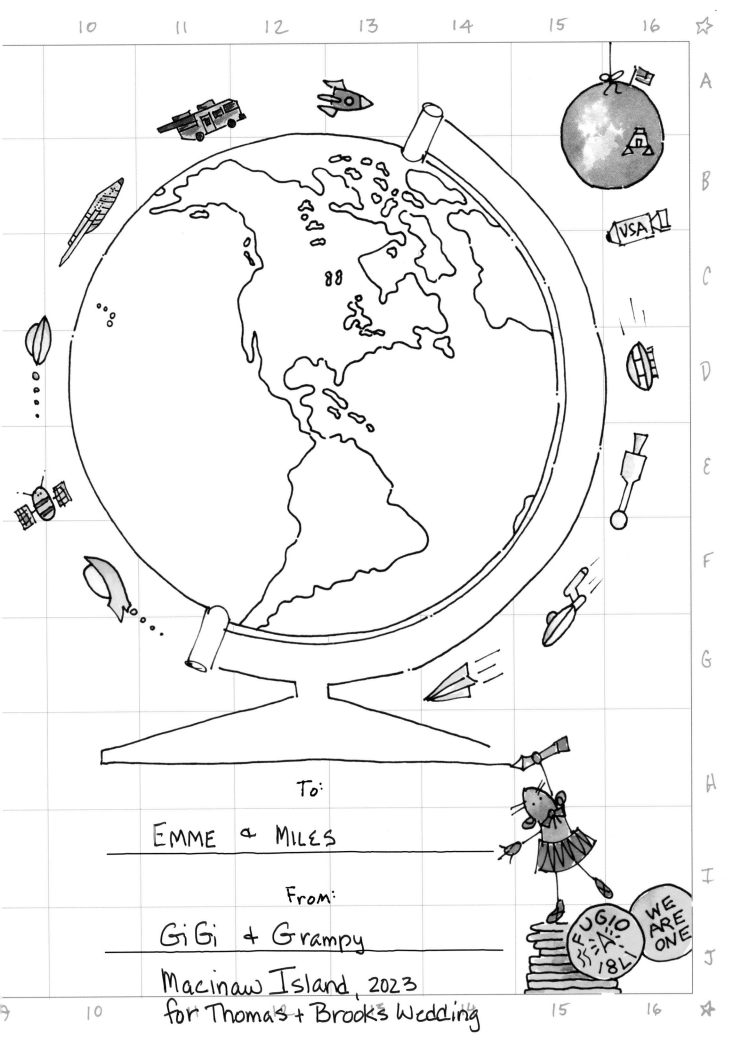

To:

EMME & MILES

From:

GiGi & Grampy

Macinaw Island, 2023
for Thomas + Brook's Wedding

⭐

A special thanks to you, the reader, the explorer,
wherever you are. Have fun checking out our journey.

For my children Austin and Breanna.
"Never give up, never surrender!" :) ... xxoo Mom

To my family, Ana Mae and Pirate Paul,
my siblings Michael, Steven, Catherine and Philip.

Uncle Al, Liz, Ron Ward and Jackie DeCosmo-Williams,
thank you for all the encouragement.

And a very special thanks to my countrymen.
I love us, flaws and all.
God Bless America :) and all that jazz.

⭐

Kirk's note and thanks.
To my wife Sandy and
my daughters Brittney and Mandy.
All my love and affection.

ADMIRAL

Dear Reader,

This book is a non-traditional tour of the United States as seen through the eyes of my seven year old self. It is created for giggles only- because, you see... there was a time when T.V.'s had ears and roller skates had keys. That time was when I was a little girl growing up in a western suburb of Detroit, Michigan. This book is not a complete collection of facts and figures of the United States - that would take way too long to draw and color and I'd rather giggle.

My parents, Pirate Paul and Ana Mae Mouse, used to take us kids on car rides after church. It was fun being in the car with my siblings. We kind of lived out in the country, the suburbs that is... so there was plenty to see, rolling hills, lakes and trees. Creating this book has been quite the trip, I have learned so much more about our beautiful country than I ever knew before.

It has been fun touring the United States via the information super highway, a.k.a. the interweb, books, DVD's etc. It is my hope that this book inspires you and your family on your own special adventures.

With hugs and kisses,
AnnieMarie Mouse

NATIONAL SYMBOLS

Flower - Red rose
(Rosa, Rosaceae, or the flower it bears)

Bird - American Bald Eagle
(Haliaeetus leucocephalus)

Tree - Oak Tree
(Quercus - 90 species in U.S.A.)

Mammal - North American Bison (Buffalo)
(Bison, bison)

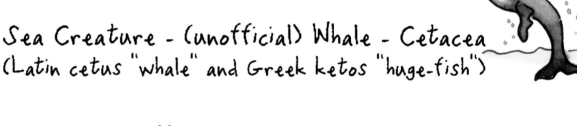

Sea Creature - (unofficial) Whale - Cetacea
(Latin cetus "whale" and Greek ketos "huge-fish")

Reptiles - (unofficial) Alligators and Crocodiles
(Reptilia)

Wildflower - (unofficial) Mayflower
(Epigaea repens / Trailing-Arbutus)

Dinosaur Fossil - (unofficial) Tyrannosaurus Rex
(tyrant lizard) October 12th is National Fossil Day!

Insect - (unofficial) - Lightning Bug or Firefly
(Family Lampyridae)

National Mottos

National Motto of the U.S.A.

"In God We Trust"

(first appeared on United States coins in 1864).

Traditional Motto

"E Pluribus Unum"

Latin for "Out of many, one".

Adopted by an Act of Congress in 1782,
used on coins and paper since 1795.

In the first month of America,
my family showed to me
an eagle in an old oak tree.

*MT. DENALI (MT. McKINLEY) 3rd TALLEST MT. IN THE WORLD

In the second month of America,
my family showed to me

two reptiles wrestling

and

an eagle in an old oak tree.

In the third month of America,
my family showed to me

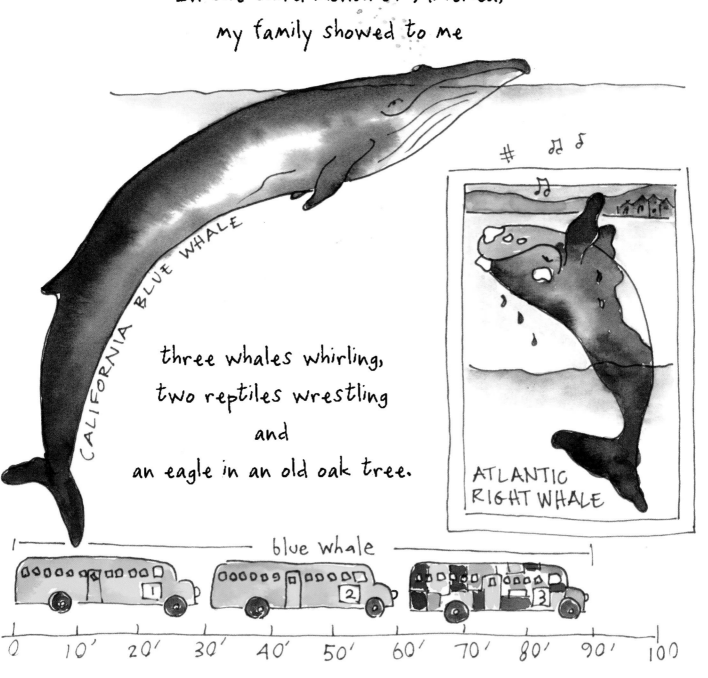

three whales whirling,
two reptiles wrestling
and
an eagle in an old oak tree.

In the fourth month of America,
my family showed to me

the Kings of Colling-wood

four roses blooming,
three whales whirling,
two reptiles wrestling
and an eagle in an
old oak tree.

GREENLAN[D]

BEAUFORT SEA

BAFFIN BAY

GULF OF ALASKA

PACIFIC OCEAN

Hawaii

GRAND CANYON

GREAT SMOKY NAT. PARK SALAMANDER

ATLAN[TIC] OCE[AN]

GULF OF MEXICO

① Great Divide
② Great Plains
③ Great Salt Lake
④ Great Salt Basin
⑤ Great Smoky National Park

In the fifth month of America, my family showed to me

FIVE GREAT LAKES!
four roses blooming, three whales whirling,
two reptiles wrestling
and an eagle in an old oak tree.

In the sixth month of America, my family showed to me

six minds inventing,
FIVE GREAT LAKES!
four roses blooming, three whales whirling,
two reptiles wrestling and an eagle in an old oak tree.

AC = ALTERNATING CURRENT = TESLA
DC = DIRECT CURRENT = EDISON

In the seventh month of America, my family showed to me

GRAND UNION

13 STRIPES
13 STARS
1776

30'
1814
←42'→
15 STARS
15 STRIPES
THE STAR
SPANGLED BANNER

OLD GLORY
34 STARS
13 STRIPES
CAPTAIN DRIVER'S FLAG
1824

37 STARS
13 STRIPES
CENTENNIAL
1876

50 STARS
13 STRIPES
1959

JULY 1969

seven flags a-flying, six minds inventing,
FIVE GREAT LAKES!
four roses blooming, three whales whirling, two reptiles wrestling
and
an eagle in an old oak tree.

In the eighth month of America, my family showed to me

eight cars a-cruising,
seven flags a-flying, six minds inventing,
FIVE GREAT LAKES!
four roses blooming, three whales whirling, two reptiles wrestling
and an eagle in an old oak tree.

In the ninth month of America, my family showed to me

nine sports a-playing,
eight cars a-cruising, seven flags a-flying, six minds inventing,
FIVE GREAT LAKES!
four roses blooming, three whales whirling, two reptiles wrestling,
and an eagle in an old oak tree.

*ONE OF THE OLDEST TEAM SPORTS IN NORTH AMERICA

OCTOBER

In the tenth month of America, my family showed to me

ten roads a-rambling, nine sports a-playing,
eight cars a-cruising, seven flags a-flying, six minds inventing,
FIVE GREAT LAKES!
four roses blooming, three whales whirling, two reptiles wrestling
and
an eagle in an old oak tree.

In the eleventh month of America, my family showed to me

eleven bison a-blazing,
ten roads a-rambling, nine sports a-playing,
eight cars a-cruising, seven flags a-flying, six minds inventing,

FIVE GREAT LAKES!

four roses blooming, three whales whirling, two reptiles wrestling
and an eagle in an old oak tree.

In the twelfth month of America, my family showed to me

twelve singers singing,
eleven bison a-blazing, ten roads a-rambling, nine sports a-playing,
eight cars a-cruising, seven flags a-flying, six minds inventing,
FIVE GREAT LAKES!
four roses blooming, three whales whirling, two reptiles wrestling
and an eagle in an old oak tree.

TURN

So long for now, reader!

Go to... www.thepeartreepress.com,
let us know what's GREAT about your "State" or have
fun with downloadable original music, videos, cartoons for
coloring and other crafts.

Looking forward to hearing from you,
AnnieMarie Mouse

"Thanks Ben!"

"Tell me and I forget, teach me and I may remember, involve me
and I learn." - Benjamin Franklin